MARTIN
COMIC & CU
WORDS BY AN

LONDON
VICTOR GOLLANCZ LTD
1989

First published in Great Britain 1979
by Victor Gollancz Ltd
14 Henrietta Street, London WC2E 8QJ

Comic & Curious Cats: the Postcard Book
First published 1989

ISBN 0 575 04632 5

Printed in Singapore by Imago Publishing Limited

FOREWORD

A bestseller in both hard and soft covers, and in the recent miniature edition, *Comic & Curious Cats* has been translated into seven languages and has sold nearly a quarter of a million copies worldwide. First published in 1979, this classic amongst cat books is now available as a collection of fine-quality postcards and also as a sumptuous book of posters. Delightful to send, purr-fect to keep – these charismatic cats are irresistible!

Martin Leman was born in London in 1934. He was for twenty years Lecturer in Design at Hornsey College of Art, before leaving to devote more time to painting. He has since gained an international reputation as the most sophisticated of 'naive' painters. Among the chief influences on his work he names early American folk art and the paintings of Henri Rousseau. Martin Leman is married and lives in London.

Angela Carter is one of Britain's most outstanding writers. The author of eight novels and three collections of stories, she has won both the Somerset Maugham Award and the James Tait Black Memorial Prize. Her short story *The Company of Wolves* was made into a successful film for which she also wrote the script.

I love my cat with an

A

Because he is Amiable
Amenable
Altogether Adorable
His name is Abednigo
He lives in Appletreewick
He Artfully eats Artichokes

PUBLISHED BY VICTOR GOLLANCZ LTD

I love my cats with a
B and a C

Because they are Beautiful
And Capricious
Beatific if Clamorous
Brisk yet Calm
Their names are
Basil and Clarissa
They live in Brandon Creek
And they eat Begonias
And Carnations
To my Bewildered
Consternation

PUBLISHED BY VICTOR GOLLANCZ LTD

I love my cat with a

D

Because he is Diabolic
Dramatic
And Debonair
His name is Dominic
He lives in Diss
He Daringly eats Dragees
Devilled Drumsticks
And Doughnuts
(Although he leaves the holes)

PUBLISHED BY VICTOR GOLLANCZ LTD

I love my cat with an

E

Although she is Elephantine
Epicurean
And Edacious
Her name is Emilia
She lives in Edgware
And she eats
Everything Earnestly

PUBLISHED BY VICTOR GOLLANCZ LTD

I love my cats with an

F and a G

Because they are
Fleet and Gracile
Flirtatious
And Gourmandising
If Freakish and Garrulous
Their names are
Francesca and Gordon
They live in FotherinGay
Frequently and Gladly
They eat Fried Fish
And Gobstoppers
With Forks and Gloves

PUBLISHED BY VICTOR GOLLANCZ LTD

I love my cat with an

H

In spite of his Hypochondria
Because he is Handsome
And Humane
His name is Horatio
He lives in Hastings
He eats Herrings, Hake
And Haddock Happily

PUBLISHED BY VICTOR GOLLANCZ LTD

I love my cat with a
JKL

Because she is Joking,
Kindly, Loving
Jumping, Kinetic,
Light-footed
Judicious, Knowing, Lyrical
Her name is JacKieLynn
She lives in
Klapham Junction, London
She eats Jellybabies
Kohlrahbi and Liquorice
Just as Quick as Lightning

PUBLISHED BY VICTOR GOLLANCZ LTD

I love my cats with an
MNO

Because they are Merry,
Neat and Oscillating
Madcap, Necessary
And Ostentatious
Moody, Notorious
And Omnivorous
Their names are Mildred,
Norman and Oliver
They live in
Midsomer NortOn
They eat Meatpies,
Nut-cutlets, Oranges
And Much else besides,
Not all of it Official

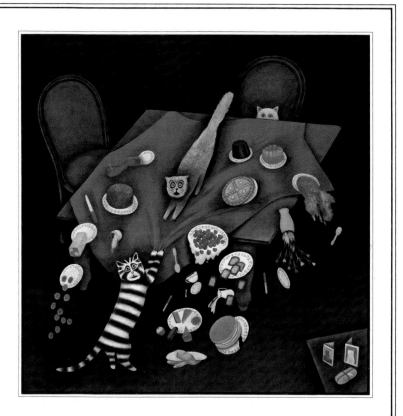

PUBLISHED BY VICTOR GOLLANCZ LTD

I love my cat with a

P and a Q

Because he is Provocative
And Questioning
Pertinacious
And Quick-sighted
Though Prone to Quest
His name is PasQuale
He moved to Puddletown
From Queen Camel
He eats Partridge,
Quince jelly
And Queen of Puddings
Purring Querulously

PUBLISHED BY VICTOR GOLLANCZ LTD

I love my cat with an

RST

Because he is Rational,
Sensitive and Tractable
Regal, Serene and Tolerant
Robust, Sincere
And Thoughtful
His name is
Raymond Stafford-Tracey
He lives in Rooms
In Stoke-on-Trent
He eats Raspberries,
Strawberries
And Toad-in-the-hole
He Rarely Seems Troubled

PUBLISHED BY VICTOR GOLLANCZ LTD

I love my cat with a

U

Although he is Ungrateful
Ugly
And Untrustworthy
His name is Unwin
He lives in Ullapool
And eats Up all the
Leftovers Ungraciously

PUBLISHED BY VICTOR GOLLANCZ LTD

I love my cat with a

V

Because he is Vigorous
Versatile
Never Vindictive
His name is Vivaldi
He lives in Virkie
He eats his Vegetables
For the sake of the Vitamins

PUBLISHED BY VICTOR GOLLANCZ LTD

I love my cat with a

W

Because he is Watchful
And Wakeful
Although he
Sometimes Worries
His name is Wilberforce
He lives in West Wittering
He eats Watercress, Windfalls –
Whatever he can get
Wistfully Winking

PUBLISHED BY VICTOR GOLLANCZ LTD

I love my cat with an

XYZ

There is really
Nothing more
To be said

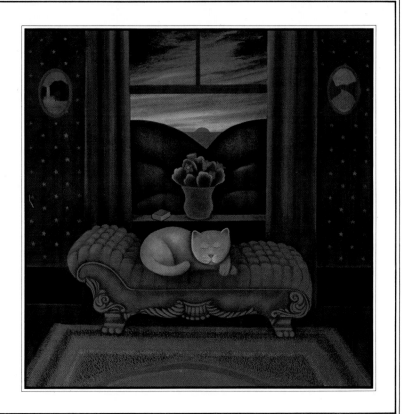

PUBLISHED BY VICTOR GOLLANCZ LTD

I love my cat with an

Because he is Amiable
Amenable
Altogether Adorable
His name is Abednigo
He lives in Appletreewick
He Artfully eats Artichokes

PUBLISHED BY VICTOR GOLLANCZ LTD

I love my cats with a

B and a C

Because they are Beautiful
And Capricious
Beatific if Clamorous
Brisk yet Calm
Their names are
Basil and Clarissa
They live in Brandon Creek
And they eat Begonias
And Carnations
To my Bewildered
Consternation

PUBLISHED BY VICTOR GOLLANCZ LTD

I love my cat with a

D

Because he is Diabolic
Dramatic
And Debonair
His name is Dominic
He lives in Diss
He Daringly eats Dragees
Devilled Drumsticks
And Doughnuts
(Although he leaves the holes)

PUBLISHED BY VICTOR GOLLANCZ LTD

I love my cat with an
E

Although she is Elephantine
Epicurean
And Edacious
Her name is Emilia
She lives in Edgware
And she eats
Everything Earnestly

PUBLISHED BY VICTOR GOLLANCZ LTD

I love my cats with an
F and a G

Because they are
Fleet and Gracile
Flirtatious
And Gourmandising
If Freakish and Garrulous
Their names are
Francesca and Gordon
They live in FotherinGay
Frequently and Gladly
They eat Fried Fish
And Gobstoppers
With Forks and Gloves

PUBLISHED BY VICTOR GOLLANCZ LTD

I love my cat with an

H

In spite of his Hypochondria
Because he is Handsome
And Humane
His name is Horatio
He lives in Hastings
He eats Herrings, Hake
And Haddock Happily

PUBLISHED BY VICTOR GOLLANCZ LTD

I love my cat with an

I

Because he is Ingenious
Ingenuous
And Insinuating
His name is Inigo
He lives in Inverurie
He eats Inkfish Incessantly

PUBLISHED BY VICTOR GOLLANCZ LTD

I love my cat with a
JKL

Because she is Joking,
Kindly, Loving
Jumping, Kinetic,
Light-footed
Judicious, Knowing, Lyrical
Her name is JacKieLynn
She lives in
Klapham Junction, London
She eats Jellybabies
Kohlrahbi and Liquorice
Just as Quick as Lightning

PUBLISHED BY VICTOR GOLLANCZ LTD

I love my cats with an

MNO

Because they are Merry,
Neat and Oscillating
Madcap, Necessary
And Ostentatious
Moody, Notorious
And Omnivorous
Their names are Mildred,
Norman and Oliver
They live in
Midsomer NortOn
They eat Meatpies,
Nut-cutlets, Oranges
And Much else besides,
Not all of it Official

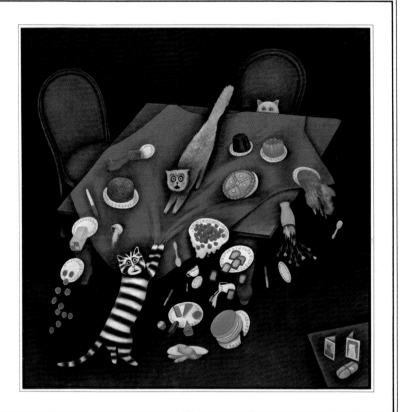

PUBLISHED BY VICTOR GOLLANCZ LTD

I love my cat with a

P and a Q

Because he is Provocative
And Questioning
Pertinacious
And Quick-sighted
Though Prone to Quest
His name is PasQuale
He moved to Puddletown
From Queen Camel
He eats Partridge,
Quince jelly
And Queen of Puddings
Purring Querulously

PUBLISHED BY VICTOR GOLLANCZ LTD

I love my cat with an

RST

Because he is Rational,
Sensitive and Tractable
Regal, Serene and Tolerant
Robust, Sincere
And Thoughtful
His name is
Raymond Stafford-Tracey
He lives in Rooms
In Stoke-on-Trent
He eats Raspberries,
Strawberries
And Toad-in-the-hole
He Rarely Seems Troubled

PUBLISHED BY VICTOR GOLLANCZ LTD

I love my cat with a

U

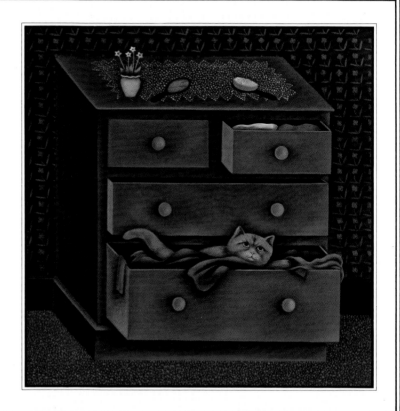

Although he is Ungrateful
Ugly
And Untrustworthy
His name is Unwin
He lives in Ullapool
And eats Up all the
Leftovers Ungraciously

PUBLISHED BY VICTOR GOLLANCZ LTD

I love my cat with a

V

Because he is Vigorous
Versatile
Never Vindictive
His name is Vivaldi
He lives in Virkie
He eats his Vegetables
For the sake of the Vitamins

PUBLISHED BY VICTOR GOLLANCZ LTD

I love my cat with a

W

Because he is Watchful
And Wakeful
Although he
Sometimes Worries
His name is Wilberforce
He lives in West Wittering
He eats Watercress, Windfalls –
Whatever he can get
Wistfully Winking

PUBLISHED BY VICTOR GOLLANCZ LTD

I love my cat with an

XYZ

There is really
Nothing more
To be said

PUBLISHED BY VICTOR GOLLANCZ LTD